TAMESIDE LIBRARIES

3 8016 01432 0446

D0348051

www. Tameside

HYDE LIBRARY
0161-342 4450

TAMESIDE LIBRARIES

- 1 MAY 2013

WITHDRAWN FROM
TAMESIDE LIBRARIES

Tony Foels

Wang Foo
the
Kung Fu Shrew

TAMESIDE M.B.C. LIBRARIES	
01432044	
Bertrams	21.02.07
J821/08	£4.50
.914	

Wang Foo
the
Kung Fu Shrew
And Other Freaky Poems Too

by

Chris White

Illustrated by the author

The King's England Press
2001

ISBN 1 872438 68 7

Wang Foo the Kung Fu Shrew is typeset by Moose Manuscripts
in Futura Casual 17pt and published by
The King's England Press Ltd,
Cambertown House, Commercial Road, Goldthorpe,
Rotherham, South Yorkshire, S63 9BL

Text and illustrations © Chris White 2001

All rights reserved. No part of this publication may be
reproduced, copied, stored in any retrieval system, or
circulated in any manner whatsoever without the express
prior written permission of the publisher.

This book is sold subject to the condition that it shall not, by
way of trade or otherwise, be lent, re-sold, hired out or
otherwise circulated without the publisher's prior consent in
any form of binding or cover than that in which it is
published and without a similar condition including this
condition being imposed on the subsequent purchaser.

The author/illustrator asserts his moral right to be recognised
as such under the terms of the Berne Convention and the
Copyright, Designs and Patents Act 1988 (as amended).

Printed and bound in Great Britain by

Woolnough Bookbinding
Irthlingborough
Northamptonshire

Foreword

Today's word is 'encouragement'. After *Bitey the Veggie Vampire* was published last year I was amazed - it was a book that was never meant to be a book.

A year on and I'm still amazed! People saying how much they enjoy *Bitey* has encouraged me beyond belief and the question "When's the next one?" really gets the juices flowing!

So here is a book that *is* meant to be a book and you really only have yourselves to blame. If you hadn't egged me on, none of this would have happened; no resurrection of Bitey, no birth of Elvis and no arrival of Wang Foo.

Encouragement is a wonderful thing. So, here we go: seconds out, round two! Just watch out for those pideys!

Mr. Foo Sends Mucho Thankos to...

Everybody who bought, read, supported and spread the word of Bitey. This one's especially for shrew.

Big thanks and kung fu karma to the three Pressketeers. Special thanks to Nic, the quiver in my lip. No thanks at all to the pideys!

Wang Foo the Kung Fu Shrew

I'll tell you a story that you won't believe,
But it happened, just last week.
I was out in the park, it was just getting dark,
All the lights had come on in the street.

I strolled on the grass past a girl with her dog
And a pair on a bench who were kissing,
When shattering the hush, leaping out of a bush,
Came a huge cat, wailing and hissing.

On closer inspection I saw in its paws
What looked like a mouse or a rat.
They were kicking and fighting, scratching and biting,
"GET OFF HIM!" I yelled at the cat.

Both carried on scrapping. "Poor little thing!"
I thought, "I must intervene.
It's not right at all for a creature that small
To be picked on by something so mean!"

But when I looked closer that wasn't the case,
I'd got it the wrong way round,
The mouse was fighting back, it was on the attack,
And soon threw the cat to the ground!

It grabbed the poor pussy in its tiny paws
And spun him above its small head,
And despite his large size, if he'd not got nine lives,
I swear that the cat would be dead!

Fur flying everywhere, I looked on,
Feeling stunned and amazed.
With a THWAK! and a THOK! a WHACK! and a
SOK! The cat lay, tongue out, both eyes glazed.

The rodent vanished into the night
Leaving a small calling card.
With great expectation I hoped for explanation
As to why this mouse was so hard.

I slowly read the tiny words:
"Is your cat evil? If so, here's what to do.
Don't hesitate, before it's too late,
Call WANG FOO, THE KUNG FU SHREW."

"Cats with attitude a speciality,
No job too big or too small.
Pedigree or shabby, Persian or Tabby,
Wang Foo will take on them all!"

I searched in the shadows to see where he went
But the light was starting to fade.
Out there in the night, filling felines with fright,
Is a rodent renegade.

It's since been whispered, behind closed doors,
That somewhere, in these parts,
Is a hero for all, standing three inches tall,
A shrew trained in martial arts.

I've hung on to his number so I know what to do
If my cat is a problem at all.
If it causes mice harm, or scratches my arm,
I'll give Wang Foo a call!

Hello!

Hi! Hello! How are you?
I hope you are okay.
Thanks a lot for finding time
To read my poems today.

There's tales of slugs and centipedes,
An ugly baby, a dead cat,
A mountain goat, the veggie vampire
And, wait..., did you hear that?

Something scuttled across the floor.
Look! It's over there!
With two big eyes, eight long legs,
And short, spiky black hair.

I think it is a pidey,
The horriblest of creatures,
That creeps round in the shadows,
Just ask your mums and teachers.

I think it's winking at me
And sticking out its tongue.
Pideys make me nervous,
But we have to carry on.

We'll try to plod on as best we can,
But PLEASE keep your eye out,
And if you see one anywhere,
Be sure to stand and shout:

"PIDEY!   PIDEY!   PIDEY!"

Rusty the Squirrel

Rusty the grey squirrel
Has been lazy all his life.
He'd never go collecting nuts
To feed his kids and wife.

"Instead of trekking round the woods
I'll nip to the shop," he boasted,
"And buy a family-sized bag of
Ready salted or dry roasted!"

Goldfish

I had a goldfish in a bowl,
I won him at the fair.
Today I went to feed him,
But my goldfish wasn't there!

He'd left me a goodbye note
Which said, "I can't stand any more.
I've taken my piano,
And gone on a world tour."

To be honest, I'm glad he's gone,
That fish was off the rails.
He kept me awake all night long,
Practising his scales.

Bitey: the Vampire Bites Back

Blow your sniffling nostrils,
And wipe your teary eye
For it seems the veggie vampire,
Didn't really die!

Bitey walks amongst us,
He's alive, for goodness' sake!
Whoever said he's dead's dead wrong,
The whole thing one missed steak!

The world's only meat-free vampire
For a while there looked doomed,
But you know how some exaggerate
A tiny little wound,

And despite his awkward accident,
Bitey looks alright:
His hair slicked back, his eyes blood-shot,
His skin a deathly white.

"I think I'm going to be okay,
But just so there's no doubt,
I'll visit the doctor's surgery
So he can check me out."

Although he didn't like going
Bitey thought, "Be brave!
It's not every day you die,
Then rise up from the grave!"

Bitey sat in the waiting room,
Dreaming of crackers and cheese,
But his thoughts of food were burst
When the nurse yelled, "NECKS PLEASE!"

"Good evening," said a hairy thing,
"It's nice to have you back!"
The thing was Bitey's doctor,
Last name Hill, first name Jack.

Dr. Hill took Bitey's pulse,
Just like yours or mine,
But vampires don't have one,
So that was a waste of time!

Then, in went a thermometer,
Which came out freezing cold.
(You don't have a lot of body heat
When you're over three centuries old!)

Next, Bitey was placed on the scales,
They said he was overweight -
That must be all the Linda McCartney
Shepherd's pies he ate!

And finally, a blood test,
Which Bitey found quite sore,
Until he glimpsed a drop of blood
And passed out on the floor!

Summing up the doctor said,
"There's nothing wrong with you!
You're in quite good condition
For a man of three hundred and two!"

So Bitey left the surgery,
Feeling quite upbeat,
And the veggie vampire's thoughts soon turned
To having a bite to eat.

"Some celebratory slap-up nosh!"
The vampire did squeal.
"A pasta bake, some lentil soup,
A nice quorn ready-meal!"

Under cover of moonlight
To a restaurant he did trot,
The waiter gave Bitey a menu,
Bitey said, "Fangs a lot!"

He carefully perused the options,
Deciding what to eat,
Checking each dish carefully
To be sure it wasn't meat.

But, I'm afraid, Bitey's meal didn't go well
In fact, he ended up dead!
It's not wise for a veggie vampire
To have a starter of garlic bread!

But although you might think that this was the end,
Please don't curse or frown.
You'd be batty to think that garlic bread
Can keep a veggie vampire down!

Duck in a Hat

Aosius good n

A duck waddled into my room today,
Sat down on the bed, and looked like it would stay.

It was wearing a tie and a small bowler hat,
It stared right towards me and, wait! What was that?

Anyway, this duck switched the radio on
And started to sing its favourite song.

I thought it was strange as it moved up beside me
And, hang on! Look! There!

PIDEY!   PIDEY!   PIDEY!

Elvis the Ugly Baby

"My God, you are ugly!" were the first words he heard,
As the hospital ward went wild.
And it has to be said that the doctor was right -
It was one *ugly* child.

He lay in his cot, dribbling and gurgling,
The nurses brought blankets of cotton.
He was so ugly it took half an hour
To work out which end was his bottom.

His parents still loved him, thought he was cute,
Well, that's what the both of them said,
They called their son Elvis 'cos he had no hair,
Except for a quiff on his head.

They took him for walks in their local park,
He threw bread for the ducks,
But the ducks just threw the bread straight back
When they saw his hideous looks.

Other parents would peer in his pram
Then run away real quick,
And if they'd recently had a meal
Odds on they'd be sick.

The old Playschool was the grandest building
You had ever seen,
Huge windows, polished floors,
The odd old wooden beam.

Its crumbling walls had seen some kids,
Some pleasant, some making a fuss,
But was this old Playschool ready for one
That looked like the back end of a bus?

On his first morning there Elvis couldn't wait
To draw and build and paint,
But the other kids would cry and scream,
And most of the teachers would faint.

His parents would not give up, though,
They sent him back once more.
"Our son deserves to build with blocks,
And read and play and draw!"

Again the classroom erupted,
His classmates yelled and cried,
And when Elvis met the class hamster,
The hamster keeled over and died!

The teachers called a meeting,
And to the parents they said,
"The only way we can have your son back
Is if he comes with a bag on his head."

Elvis' parents trudged out of the school,
To break the news to their son.
And there was Elvis, smiling and jumping,
Having so much fun.

"What's happened darling?" Mother asked,
"I've never seen you so happy!"
Elvis just smiled a contented smile
Then did a brown mess in his nappy.

The reason that Elvis was satisfied
Was that he'd found a friend,
Someone who'd stick right by his side
Until the bitter end.

"WHAT IS IT?" screamed his father,
"It looks like a giant blister!"
"No," said the nurse that was holding it,
"It's Elvis' ugly sister."

"It turns out that you have had twins,
We thought that perhaps, maybe,
She might be yours but it took this long
To work out it was a baby!"

So there they were, the ugly twins,
A sister and a brother,
Both now happy to be ugly,
'Cos they look as bad as each other.

They play together, blissfully happy,
Running round the park.
They just don't mix with other kids,
And go out when it's dark.

And the old Playschool is quiet once more,
From its floor to its intricate gilding,
Because Elvis has left the reading and painting
And Elvis has left the building!

Ode to a Dead Cat

My cat is dead! My cat is dead!
Poor kitty is no more.
He's starting to whiff, he's cold and he's stiff,
Lying on the kitchen floor.

My cat is gone! My cat is gone!
Old kitty is starting to harden.
He's flat out in his tray, but soon he will lay
In a hole at the end of the garden.

Carol

Carol the worm had no friends, I'm afraid,
Her life was one long toil.
She longed for another to burrow along
And join her in the soil.

Days turned to weeks, turned to months, turned to years,
And Carol was still alone.
No other worms came calling
At her quiet underground home.

So one day Carol took action and cried,
"I think that I have earned
My right to be happy and not miserable.
Today, this worm has turned!"

Carol's a different worm these days,
She's got loads of friends now;
She gets to speak with them every day,
Let me tell you how:

Carol bought a PC,
And all the friends she's met
Are the product of being the world's first worm
To be on the Internet!

Slug and Centipede

There was once this slug and this centipede
And it really was no joke
The money problems that they had –
These insects were flat broke.

They hatched a plan together
To try and make things right;
The plan was to rob the local bank,
Late on Tuesday night.

The slug and the centipede talked it through
So there wasn't any mistake.
They planned it all so carefully,
From the break-in to their escape.

That Tuesday night, while other bugs
Were tucked up in their beds,
Slug and centipede were in the bank
With tights upon their heads.

The slug couldn't carry much money
But the plan still worked like a charm
'Cos the centipede shoved a big bag of cash
Under every arm.

They got away with thousands
And they thought that that was that,
But, I'm afraid, the police planned a raid
On their East End flat.

The police, you see, found two clues
So the insects' chances were slim;
The centipede left many fingerprints
And the slug left a trail behind him!

Get Your Room Clean!

My Mum's told me to get my room clean,
She says it's the biggest tip she's ever seen.
It's cluttered with books and comics and toys.
Hang on a second, what was that noise?

It isn't, is it? No, it couldn't be!
I'll just ignore it 'cos I want my tea,
And I won't get any if this room's not tidy.
Wait! Yes, it is!

PIDEY!   PIDEY!   PIDEY!

Lucy Rabbit

Lucy was a rabbit,
She had so many kids,
She needed some time to herself,
So guess what Lucy did?

She got a baby-sitter in,
Jumped into her car,
Then drove into town and
Sang all night in a karaoke bar!

Lucy was a rabbit
With one big family.
I think that since the last verse
It's gone up to twenty-three!

She felt she couldn't cope again,
She needed time off, so,
Again she got a sitter in
And went to play Bingo!

Lucy was a rabbit,
I think you know the rest,
But this time it's not Lucy
But her kids that are all stressed.

"Mum, we never see you much!
You disappear for hours!"
So that week-end she took them all
On a trip to Alton Towers.

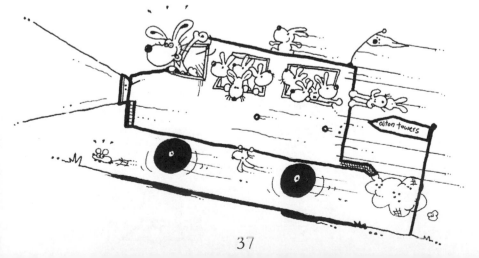

The Little Blue Lion

Many, many miles away,
Where the land is hard and dry
And there's no escape from the sun,
Burning in the sky,

There is a pride of lions
Living there together,
They eat and sleep and live their lives
Enjoying the good weather.

Most of the lions are happy,
Except one little guy;
The other lions don't like him much -
Let me tell you why.

They laugh and point and snigger,
They shout names at him too.
The reason he gets picked on is
His fur is coloured blue.

Whilst all the other lions are golden,
With a brownish mane,
For some reason, we don't know why,
This lion is not the same.

When he takes a stroll through the jungle
The hyenas stop and laugh,
And it's a great big pain in the neck
To be ridiculed by a giraffe.

It makes the little lion cry,
He doesn't think it's fair
That he should be picked on
Because he's got different hair.

Then, one day, a bright red parrot
Squawked down from her nest:
"I think that you should be quite pleased
You don't look like the rest!"

"Yes! You're right! It's not my fault
That I am blue, not brown!
From now on I'll ignore the taunts,
I won't take this lion down!

From this day on I'll stand up tall
And roar my message loud!
I like the fact that I am blue -
I stand out in a crowd!"

"Besides, it's not my colour,
But the lion I am inside.
When I walk through the jungle,
I'll wear my fur with pride!"

And now the other animals
Don't laugh when he walks by
Because the little blue lion
Holds his little blue head high.

Whereas before they'd shout and point,
And call him a blue freak,
Now he's the main attraction,
He's one of a kind, he's unique!

Dinner

Do you ever stop and think about
The food that's on your plate?
Like, do they use real nans
In that naan bread you just ate?
And how about shepherd's pie,
Are there real shepherds inside?
Just think about the rioting sheep
About the countryside
And what about toad-in-the-hole?
Is it really made from toads,
That are scraped up off the tarmac,
From Britain's major roads?
And then there are fish-fingers,
Is this really a dish,
That's made from chopping off
The hands of somebody's pet fish?
I think that we should all be told,
I really think we oughta,
And until I know all the facts
I'll stick to bread and water!

Pidey! Pidey! Pidey!

When you want to have a long hot bath
And you're standing on the rug,
Just starting to run the hot tap,
What's sitting near the plug?

Pidey! Pidey! Pidey!

If you're trying to get to sleep at night,
You've got that peepy feeling,
What's lurking in the darkness,
Hanging from the ceiling?

Pidey! Pidey! Pidey!

When you sit down to write a letter
To your closest friend,
And pick up your favourite pen,
What's dangling on the end?

Pidey! Pidey! Pidey!

You want to go out for a walk,
With your dog in the park,
But when you look inside your shoes,
What's hiding in the dark?

Pidey! Pidey! Pidey!

If you really want to read a book
And curl up in a chair.
When you find the page you're on,
What's running round in there?

Pidey!   Pidey!   Pidey!

You're going to the cinema,
You're late and in a rush.
Check your make-up — do your hair,
But wait — what's on your brush.

Pidey!   Pidey!   Pidey!

When you want to write a poem,
And you've got some great ideas,
You're sitting down – pen in your hand,
What is it that appears?

Pidey!   Pidey!   Pidey!

My Cat Needs Glasses

I think my cat needs glasses,
'Cos when he's had a nap
He jumps out of his basket
And heads for his catflap

But instead of going through it,
His head will THWACK! the door,
And when I get home there's my cat,
Unconscious on the floor!

Simon and Sue

Simon was a worker ant
Who had a lovely wife.
The pair of ants were proud parents
And had a busy life.

So when the chance came for a night on the town
Simon and Sue couldn't wait.
They hurriedly arranged a babysitter
For their kids, all one hundred and eight.

The sitter arrived, they sped to the door,
Not giving him a glance,
And so he was left in a room for the night
Looking after all the little ants.

The hours ticked by, Sue and Simon came home,
Just imagine their shock and their pain
As they realised they'd left their kids in the care of
An ant-eater called Wayne!

Greyhounds I Have Known

It was a cosy Sunday afternoon
In the home of Grandpa Hare.
He sat under an old blanket,
In his rocking chair.

The elderly hare was worn and grey,
One of his ears was missing,
But he felt young again when the grandkids came round
To hear Grandpa reminiscing.

They'd sit in a circle surrounding his chair
And hang on every word,
Of tales of life in days gone by,
Stories they'd never heard.

You see Grandpa Hare wasn't normal,
You wouldn't know to look at his face.
He was, in fact, a mechanical hare
The sort that greyhounds race.

Grandpa had worked for many a year,
We're talking a while back,
As packs of dogs would chase him
Round the local greyhound track.

He'd been the best at what he did,
Ran circuits in record time,
And no greyhound EVER beat Grandpa Hare
In crossing that finishing line.

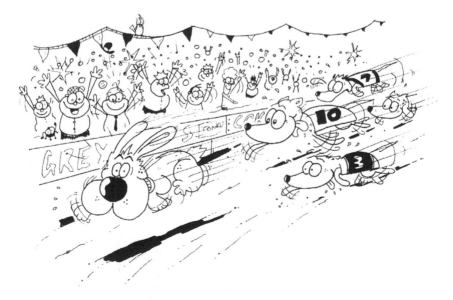

"Tell us again!" piped up one tiny hare,
"Oh, Grandpa, we'd all love to hear
Of some of the famous greyhounds
That you have beaten in your career!!"

Grandpa sat back, feeling warm and proud,
Like a king upon his throne.
"Gather round little ones and I'll tell you the names
Of the greyhounds I have known."

"Fast Jenny, Slim William, Lanky Montell,
'Round' Martha and Old Whiskered Tim.
Muzzled Pauline, Sleek Johnny, Slick Simon,
Bulbous-Eyed Eric, Lithe Jim."

"Ribby George, 'Tubby' Cedric, Leggy Katherine,
Lean Kenneth, Small-Snouted Sam.
Slender James, Small-Eared Ethel, 'Fat' Matthew
And the 50-to-1 shot, 'Big' Pam."

"There was Gaunt Features Graham and Slender Kate,
A spindly dog they called Bones.
Identical twins, 'Porky' Pat and Pat 'Porky',
And Mr. Rodney 'the whippet' Jones."

"Don't forget Swift Yvonne and Tiny Feet Jan,
Boney Bill and Whirlwind Greg.
And most bizarrely I remember this race
With a dog that had only one leg."

"Pot-Bellied Benji, Two-Headed Dave,
Who was tested for steroids, I heard,
And a greyhound they told me was owned by the
Queen Called Sir Cecil Smythe-Farquar the Third."

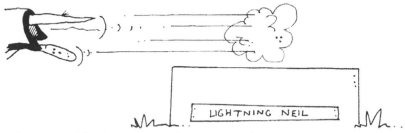

"Lightning Neil, who, whenever he ran,
Set record times for the course.
Gigantic Greg, who after inspection,
Turned out to be a small horse."

"Yes! I raced them all, and beat them!
I really was the best!
But excuse me, it's time for my afternoon nap,
Even mechanical hares need their rest!"

Brad Beaver

The beavers swam and worked
And played in the river deep.
They built their little beaver dams
In which they all could sleep.

The dams were all damn sturdy,
Could withstand storm or flood,
Except dams built by Brad Beaver -
At construction he wasn't too good.

In some dams beaver discos were held,
Where boy and girl beavers connected.
But Brad's dams were that bad, to keep them held up,
Scaffolding would be erected.

In other dams, maths lessons were taught,
Teachers and pupils would mix.
But the conclusion was always:
Strong wind + Brad's dams = big pile of sticks.

He was sick of his failures and whilst other fine homes
Held wine-tasting (with nibbles perhaps),
Brad's attempts to woo lovers or watch tv with others
Would end with his home in collapse.

But those days are gone, Brad now lives in a home
Without a worry or fear.
With a few nails and glue, his home's now brand new,
A flat-pack dam from IKEA!

The Big, Big Guinea Pig

My guinea pig won't stop eating,
That's all it seems to do.
I used to feed it twice a day
But now it's twenty-two!

It's growing too big for its cage
And I think that very soon,
At the rate my guinea's growing
It will take up all my room.

I'll have to move my bed out
And all my books and toys.
Imagine what a smell there'd be
And just think of the noise.

I'd have to move it to the yard
If it grew that big.
It could scare burglars away,
My own guard guinea pig.

And if it started growing to
An even bigger size,
I'd need a Ferris wheel
To give it exercise.

But imagine how my friends would stare
And how they'd make a fuss,
When I came to school on my huge pet
Instead of on the bus.

I hope he doesn't get that big
'Cos I think, without a doubt,
It would be the worst thing in the world
To clean a giant guinea pig out!

Fang

In a place, in the woods, in the dark, in a cave,
Is a place where the bats all hang.
Most of them are vampire bats,
But not the one called Fang.

Every night at 12 o'clock
You can hear a thousands wings,
Taking little furry bats
To dine on living things.

The vampire bats go out,
To suck on cows or moths and flies.
Fang sits alone, nibbling a plum,
Then just breaks down and cries.

The other bats don't get him,
They won't give him a break.
Although he's just a fruit bat,
They call him a fruitcake.

He doesn't fancy sucking blood
Like that bloodthirsty lot.
Fang prefers some nuts or dates,
Maybe a nice kumquat!

But more than that, at the end of the day,
When he is cold and tired,
Fang longs for someone to care for him,
To be loved and desired.

Someone who understands him,
Someone to share his pain.
So off he flapped, into the night,
Flitting through the rain.

And that's the last I saw of him.
Did he find someone to care?
Who can tell, but you know what they say -
There's someone for everyone out there.

Mushtaq the Goat

A herd of hairy mountain goats
Lived high on the mountain-side.
They'd hop and skip up rocks so steep,
Jump chasms metres wide.

But Mushtaq goat wasn't nimble at all,
He wasn't what you'd call petite.
His quite podgy tummy made him look a dummy,
He wasn't the best on his feet.

Mushtaq stumbled time after time,
But didn't know what to do.
He'd slip down slopes, plummet from peaks
And ended up black and blue!

One morning he thought, "I know what must be done
So I can go where I like."
Mushtaq now gets his thrills, over mountains and hills,
On a top-of-the-range mountain bike!

I'm Bathing my Dog

I'm bathing my dog,
He's standing in a tub,
He's having a good clean
And getting a rub.

He's so wet and bedraggled
He looks like he's drowned,
But he really enjoys it -
Hang on, what's that sound?

My dog's ears just pricked up,
He heard it too,
But I'll just carry on
With his doggy shampoo.

The soap in my hands
Is all slippy and slidey.
Oh, no! Not again!
PIDEY!   PIDEY!   PIDEY!